The Essential LEONARI

Published by:
Wise Publications
8/9 Frith Street, London W1D 3JB, England.

Exclusive distributors:
Music Sales Limited
Distribution Centre, Newmarket Road,
Bury St Edmunds, Suffolk IP33 3YB, England.
Music Sales Pty Limited
120 Rothschild Avenue, Rosebery, NSW 2018, Australia.

Order No. AM977020
ISBN 1-84449-140-4
This book © Copyright 2003 by Wise Publications.

Music arrangements by Derek Jones.
Music processed by Paul Ewers Music Design.

www.musicsales.com

The Essential LEONARD COHEN

Wise Publications
part of The Music Sales Group
London / New York / Paris / Sydney / Copenhagen / Berlin / Madrid / Tokyo

Suzanne

Words & Music by Leonard Cohen

have no love to give her, Then she gets you on her

wave - length, And she lets the riv - er an - swer that you've al -

ways been her lov - er.

And you want to trav - el with her, And you

want to trav-el blind.____ And you know she will trust____

____ you, for you've touched her per-fect bod-y with your

mind.

2. And
3. Now Suz-

mind.

ritard.

2. And Jesus was a sailor
   When he walked upon the water,
   And he spent a long time watching
   From his lonely wooden tower.
   And when he knew for certain
   Only drowning men could see him,
   He said,"All men will be sailors then
   Until the sea shall free them."
   But he himself was broken,
   Long before the sky would open.
   Forsaken, almost human,
   He sank beneath your wisdom like a stone.
   And you want to travel with him,
   And you want to travel blind,
   And you think maybe you'll trust him,
   For he's touched your perfect body
       with his mind.

3. Now Suzanne takes your hand,
   And she leads you to the river.
   She is wearing rags and feathers
   From Salvation Army counters.
   And the sun pours down like honey
   On our lady of the harbour.
   And she shows you where to look
   Among the garbage and the flowers.
   There are heroes in the seaweed,
   There are children in the morning,
   They are leaning out for love,
   And they will lean that way forever.
   While Suzanne holds the mirror.
   And you want to travel with her,
   And you want to travel blind,
   And you know that you can trust her,
   For she's touched your perfect body
       with her mind.

The Stranger Song

Words & Music by Leonard Cohen

2. And then sweeping up the jokers that
      he left behind,
   You find he did not leave you very much,
   Not even laughter.
   Like any dealer, he was watching for the card
      that is so high and wild,
   He'll never need to deal another.
   He was just some Joseph looking for a
      manger,
   He was just some Joseph looking for a
      manger.

3. And then leaning on your window sill,
   He'll say one day you caused his will
   To weaken with your love and warmth
      and shelter.
   And then taking from his wallet
      an old schedule of trains, he'll say,
   "I told you when I came I was a stranger,
   I told you when I came I was a stranger."

4. But now another stranger
   Seems to want to ignore his dreams,
   As though they were the burden of some other.
   O, you've seen that kind of man before,
   His golden arm dispatching cards.
   But now it's rusted from the elbow to
      the finger,
   Yes, he wants to trade the game he knows
      for shelter.

5. You hate to watch another tired man
      lay down his hand,
      Like he was giving up the holy game of poker.
   And while he talks his dreams to sleep,
   You notice there's a highway that is
      curling up like smoke above his shoulder,
   It's curling up like smoke above his shoulder.

6. You tell him to come in, sit down,
   But something makes you turn around.
   The door is open, you can't close your shelter.
   You try the handle of the road,
   It opens, do not be afraid.
   It's you, my love, you who are the stranger,
   It's you, my love, you who are the stranger.

7. Well, I've been waiting, I was sure
   We'd meet between the trains we're waiting for,
   I think it's time to board another.
   Please understand, I never had a secret chart
   To get me to the heart
   Of this or any other matter.
   When he talks like this,
      you don't know what he's after.
   When he speaks like this,
      you don't know what he's after.

8. Let's meet tomorrow, if you choose,
   Upon the shore, beneath the bridge
   That they are building on some endless river.
   Then he leaves the platform
   For the sleeping car that's warm, you realize
   He's only advertising one more shelter.
   And it comes to you, he never was a stranger.
   And you say, "O. K., the bridge or someplace later."

9. And then sweeping up the jokers that
      he left behind,
   You find he did not leave you very much,
   Not even laughter.
   Like any dealer, he was watching for the card
      that is so high and wild,
   He'll never need to deal another.
   He was just some Joseph looking for a
      manger,
   He was just some Joseph looking for a
      manger.

10. And then leaning on your window sill,
    He'll say one day you caused his will
    To weaken with your love and warmth
       and shelter
    And then taking from his wallet
       an old schedule of trains, he'll say,
    "I told you when i came I was a stranger,
    I told you when I came I was a stranger."

17

Sisters Of Mercy

Words & Music by Leonard Cohen

20

We weren't lov - ers like that, And be - sides, it would still be all right.

ritard.

Additional Lyrics

2. Yes, you who must leave everything
   That you cannot control,
   It begins with your family,
   But soon it comes round to your soul.
   Well, I've been where you're hanging,
   I think I can see how you're pinned.
   When you're not feeling holy,
   Your loneliness says that you've sinned.

3. They lay down beside me,
   I made my confession to them.
   They touched both my eyes,
   And I touched the dew on their hem.
   If your life is a leaf
   That the seasons tear off and condemn,
   They will bind you with love
   That is graceful and green as a stem.

4. When I left, they were sleeping,
   I hope you run into them soon.
   Don't turn on the lights,
   You can read their address by the moon.
   And you won't make me jealous
   If I hear that they sweetened your night.
   We weren't lovers like that,
   And besides, it would still be all right.
   We weren't lovers like that,
   And besides, it would still be all right.

21

Hey, That's No Way To Say Goodbye

Words & Music by Leonard Cohen

23

bye.

Additional Lyrics

2. I'm not looking for another
   As I wander in my time.
   Walk me to the corner,
   Our steps will always rhyme.
   You know my love goes with you
   As your love stays with me,
   It's just the way it changes
   Like the shoreline and the sea.
   But let's not talk of love or chains
   And things we can't untie,
   Your eyes are soft with sorrow,
   Hey, that's no way to say goodbye.

3. I loved you in the morning,
   Our kisses deep and warm,
   Your hair upon the pillow,
   Like a sleepy golden storm.
   Yes, many loved before us,
   I know that we are not new,
   In city and in forest,
   They smiled like me and you.
   But let's not talk of love or chains
   And things we can't untie,
   Your eyes are soft with sorrow,
   Hey, that's no way to say goodbye.

Bird On A Wire

Words & Music by Leonard Cohen

ba - by still - born, like a beast with his horn, I have torn ev - 'ry - one____ who reached out for me.

But I swear by this song, and by all____ that I have done wrong, I will make it all up to thee.

So Long, Marianne

Words & Music by Leonard Cohen

Moderately slow, in 2

It's time that we be-gan___ to laugh and

cry and cry and laugh a - bout it

all a - gain.

2. Well,

2. Well, you know that I love to live with you,
   But you make me forget so very much.
   I forget to pray for the angel,
   And then the angels forget to pray for us.
   Chorus

3. We met when we were almost young,
   Deep in the green lilac park.
   You held on to me like I was a crucifix,
   As we went kneeling through the dark.
   Chorus

4. Your letters, they all say that you're beside me now.
   Then why do I feel alone?
   I'm standing on a ledge, and your fine spider web
   Is fastening my ankle to a stone.
   Chorus

5. For now I need your hidden love,
   I'm cold as a new razor blade.
   You left when I told you I was curious,
   I never said that I was brave.
   Chorus

6. Oh, you're really such a pretty one.
   I see you've gone and changed your name again,
   And just when I climbed this whole mountainside
   To wash my eyelids in the rain.
   Chorus

7. O your eyes, well, I forget your eyes,
   Your body's at home in every sea.
   How come you gave away your news to everyone,
   That you said was a secret for me?
   Chorus

Partisan

Words & Music by Anna Marly & Hy Zaret

1. When they poured a-cross__ the bor-
(2.) changed my name__ so of-
(Verses 3-9 see block lyrics)

2. I   have
3. An old

Verse 3:
An old woman gave us shelter
Kept us hidden in the garret
Then the soldiers came
She died without a whisper.

Verse 4:
There were three of us this morning
I'm the only one this evening
But I must go on
The frontiers are my prison.

Verse 5:
Oh, the wind, the wind is blowing
Through the graves the wind is blowing
Freedom soon will come
Then we'll come from the shadows.

Verse 6:
Les Allemands e'taient chez moi
Ils me dirent, "Signe toi"
Mais je n'ai pas peur
J'ai repris mon arme.

Verse 7:
J'ai changè cent fois de nom
J'ai perdu femme et ènfants
Mais j'ai tant d'amis
J'ai la France entière.

Verse 8:
Un vieil homme dans un grenier
Pour la nuit nous a cache
Les Allemands I'ont pris
Il est mort sans surprise.

Verse 9:
Oh, the wind, the wind is blowing
Through the graves the wind is blowing
Freedom soon will come
Then we'll come from the shadows. (*fade)*

Chelsea Hotel #2

Words & Music by Leonard Cohen

you got a - way, did - n't you, ba - by? You

just turned your back on the crowd.

You got a - way, I nev - er once heard you say, "I

need you, I don't need you, I

Additional Lyrics

2. I remember you well in the Chelsea Hotel,
   You were famous, your heart was a legend.
   You told me again you preferred handsome men,
   But for me you would make an exception.
   And clenching your fist for the ones like us
   Who are oppressed by the figures of beauty,
   You fixed yourself, you said, "Well, never mind,
   We are ugly but we have the music."
   Chorus

3. I don't mean to suggest that I loved you the best,
   I can't keep track of each fallen robin.
   I remember you well in the Chelsea Hotel,
   That's all, I don't think of you that often.

Famous Blue Raincoat

Words & Music by Leonard Cohen

I'm writ-ing you now just to see if you're bet-ter.

New York is cold, but I like where I'm liv-ing, The

mus - ic on Clin - ton Street all through the eve - ning.

I hear that you're build - ing your lit - tle

43

46

night that you planned to go clear.

Sin - cere - ly, L. Co - hen.

ritard.

Additional Lyrics

2. The last time we saw you, you looked so much older,
   Your famous blue raincoat was torn at the shoulder.
   You'd been to the station to meet ev'ry train,
   You came home without Lili Marlene.
   And you treated my woman to a flake of your life,
   And when she came back, she was nobody's wife.
Chorus: Well, I see you there with a rose in your teeth, one more thin gypsy thief.
   Well, I see Jane's away, she sends her regards.

3. And what can I tell you my brother, my killer,
   What can I possibly say?
   I guess that I miss you, I guess I forgive you,
   I'm glad you stood in my way.
   If you ever come by here for Jane or for me,
   Well, your enemy is sleeping and his woman is free.
Chorus: Yes, thanks for the trouble you took from her eyes.
   I thought it was there for good, so I never tried.

Coda: And Jane came by with a lock of your hair,
   She said that you gave it to her,
   That night that you planned to go clear.
   Sincerely, L. Cohen.

Take This Longing

Words & Music by Leonard Cohen

49

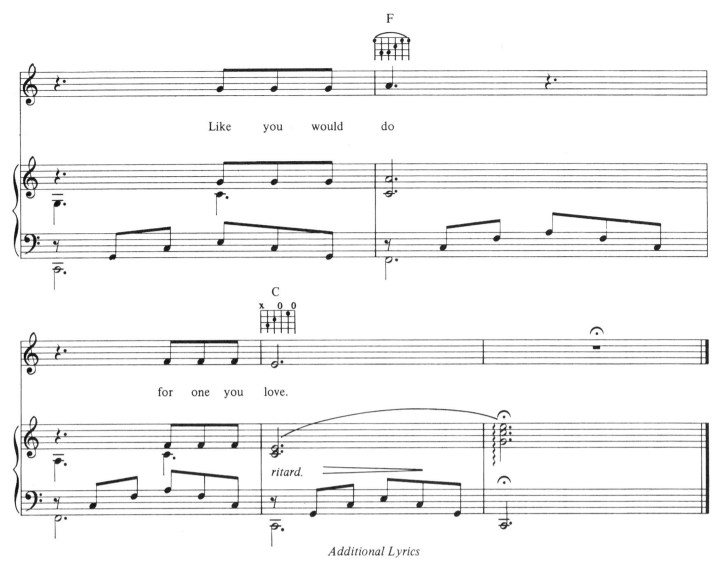

Like you would do

for one you love.

ritard.

Additional Lyrics

2. Your body like a searchlight,
   My poverty revealed.
   I would like to try your charity
   Until you cry, now you must try my greed.
   And everything depends upon
   How near you sleep to me.

Chorus: Just take this longing from my tongue,
   And all the lonely things my hands have done.
   Let me see your beauty broken down,
   Like you would do for one you love.

3. Hungry as an archway
   Through which the troops have passed.
   I stand in ruins behind you
   With your winter clothes, your broken saddle straps.
   I love to see you naked over there,
   Especially from the back.

Chorus: Ah, take this longing from my tongue,
   And all the useless things my hands have done.
   Untie for me your high blue gown,
   Like you would do for the one you love.

4. You're faithful to the better man,
   I'm afraid that he left.
   So let me judge your love affair
   In this very room where I have sentenced mine to death.
   I'll even wear these old laurel leaves
   That he's shaken from his head.

Chorus: Just take this longing from my tongue,
   And all the useless things my hands have done.
   Let me see your beauty broken down,
   Like you would do for one you love.
   Like you would do for one you love.

Who By Fire

Words & Music by Leonard Cohen

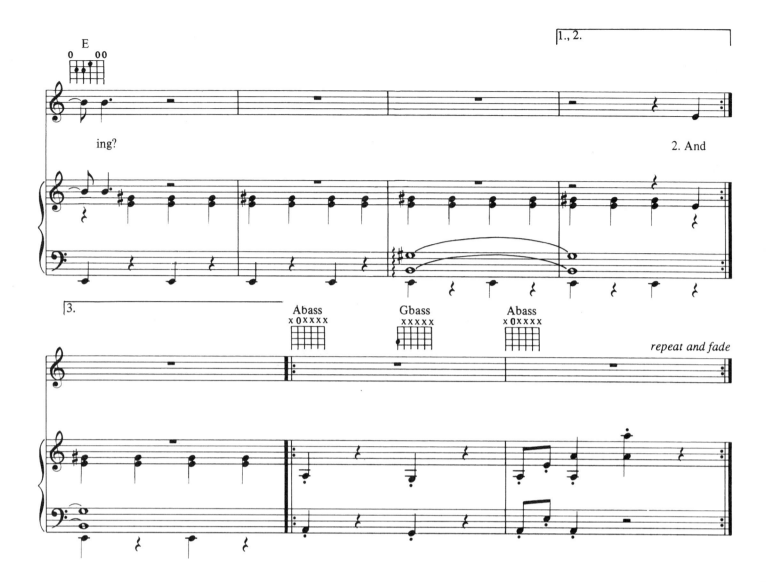

Additional Lyrics

2. And who in her lonely slip,
   Who by barbiturate?
   Who in these realms of love,
   Who by something blunt?
   Who by avalanche,
   Who by powder?
   Who for his greed,
   Who for his hunger?
   And who shall I say is calling?

3. And who by brave ascent,
   Who by accident?
   Who in solitude,
   Who in this mirror?
   Who by his lady's command,
   Who by his own hand?
   Who in mortal chains,
   Who in power?
   And who shall I say is calling?

The Guests

Words & Music by Leonard Cohen

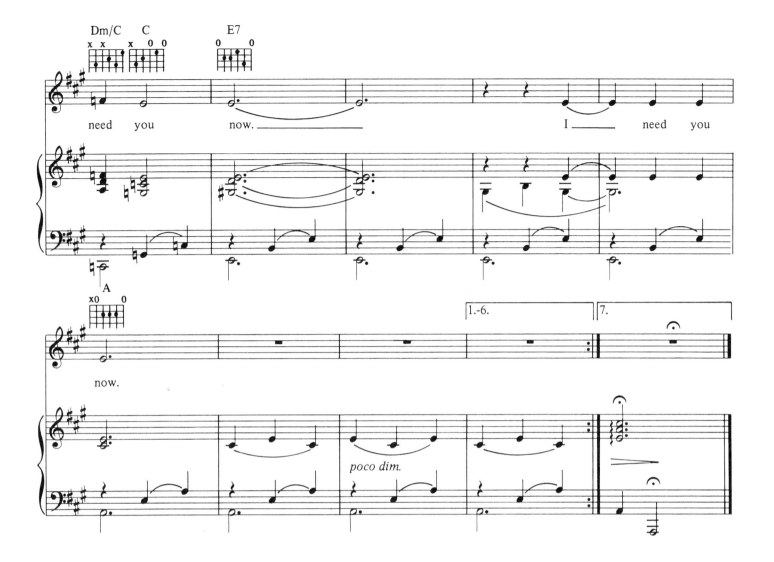

Additional Lyrics

3. And all go stumbling through that house in lonely secrecy,
Saying, "Do reveal yourself," or, "Why hast thou forsaken me?"
Chorus

4. All at once the torches flare, the inner door flies open.
One by one, they enter there in every style of passion.
Chorus

5. And here they take their sweet repast while house and grounds dissolve.
And one by one, the guests are cast beyond the garden walls.
Chorus

6. And those who dance begin to dance, those who weep begin.
And those who earnestly are lost, are lost and lost again.
Chorus

7. One by one, the guests arrive, the guests are coming through.
The broken-hearted many, the open-hearted few.

Hallelujah

Words & Music by Leonard Cohen

59

Verse 3:
You say I took the name in vain
I don't even know the name
But if I did, well really, what's it to you?
There's a blaze of light in every word
It doesn't matter which you heard
The holy or the broken Hallelujah.

Hallelujah *etc.*

Verse 4:
I did my best, it wasn't much
I couldn't feel, so I tried to touch
I've told the truth, I didn't come to fool you.
And even though it all went wrong
I'll stand before the Lord of Song
With nothing on my tongue but Hallelujah.

Hallelujah *etc.*

If It Be Your Will

Words & Music by Leonard Cohen

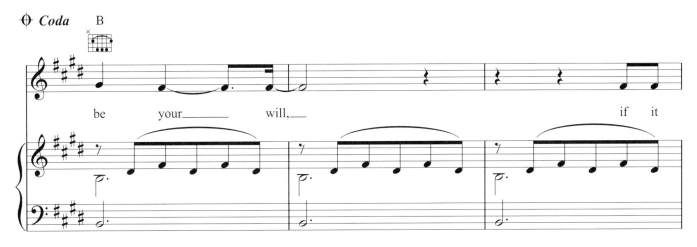

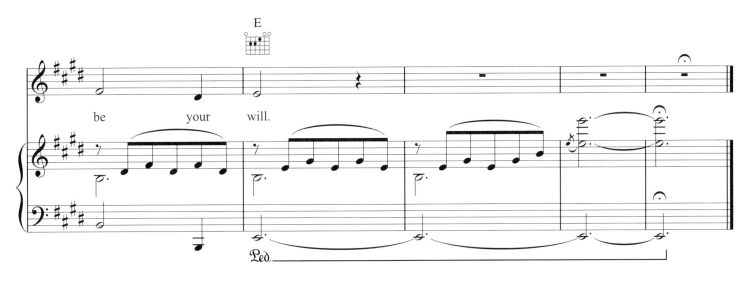

Verse 3:
If it be your will
If there is a choice
Let the rivers fill
Let the hills rejoice
Let your mercy spill
On all these burning hearts in hell
If it be your will
To make us well.

Verse 4:
And draw us near
And bind us tight
All your children here
In their rags of light
In our rags of light
All dressed to kill
And end this night
If it be your will
If it be your will.

Night Comes On

Words & Music by Leonard Cohen

down to the place___ where I knew she lay wait-ing___
(2.) fight-ing in E-gypt when they signed this a-gree-ment that

(Verses 3, 4 & 5 see block lyric)

1. I went

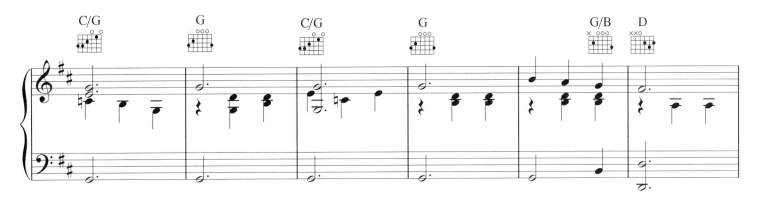

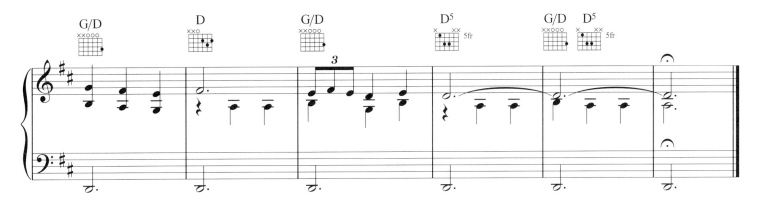

Verse 3:

We were locked in this kitchen,
I took to religion
And I wondered how long she would stay.
I needed so much
To have nothing to touch;
I've always been greedy that way.
But my son and my daughter
Climbed out of the water
Crying "Papa, you promised to play."
And they lead me away
To the great surprise,
It's "Papa, don't peek; Papa, cover your eyes."
And they hide, they hide in the world.

Verse 4:

Now I look for her always;
I'm lost in this calling,
I'm tied to the threads of some prayer.
Saying "When will she summon me,
When will she come to me,
What must I do to prepare?"
When she bends to my longing
Like a willow, like a fountain,
She stands in the luminous air.
And the night comes on,
It's very calm.
I lie in her arms; she says "When I'm gone,
I'll be yours, yours for a song."

Verse 5:

Now the crickets are singing,
The vesper bells ringing:
The cat's curled asleep in his chair.
I'll go down to Bill's Bar -
I can make it that far -
And I'll see if my friends are still there.
Yes, and here's to the few
Who forgive what you do,
And the fewer who don't even care.
And the night comes on,
It's very calm.
I want to cross over, I want to go home;
But she says "Go back, go back to the world."

I'm Your Man

Words & Music by Leonard Cohen

If you want a lov-er, I'll do an-y-thing you

72

Tower Of Song

Words & Music by Leonard Cohen

but I'm not com-ing on. I'm just

pay-ing my rent ev-ery day in the Tow-er of Song.

2. I

3. I was

4. So you can

5. Now you can

I see you stand-ing on the oth-er side.___ I don't know how the riv-er

never have to lose it again. ___ Now I

bid you farewell, ___ I don't know when I'll be back. ___ They're

moving us tomorrow to that tower down the track. But you'll be

hearing from me, baby, long after I'm gone.

I'll be speak-ing to you sweet-ly from a

win-dow in the Tow-er of Song. —

Additional Lyrics

2. I said to Hank Williams, "How lonely does it get?"
   Hank Williams hasn't answered yet.
   But I hear him coughing all night long,
   A hundred floors above me in the Tower of Song.

3. I was born like this, I had no choice.
   I was born with the gift of a golden voice.
   And twenty-seven angels from the Great Beyond,
   They tied me to this table right here in the Tower of Song.

4. So you can stick your little pins in that voodoo doll.
   I'm very sorry, baby, doesn't look like me at all.
   I'm standing by the window where the light is strong.
   They don't let a woman kill you, not in the Tower of Song.

5. Now you can say that I've grown bitter, but of this you may be sure:
   The rich have got their channels in the bedrooms of the poor.
   And there's a mighty judgment coming, but I may be wrong.
   You see, you hear these funny voices in the Tower of Song.

Everybody Knows

Words & Music by Leonard Cohen & Sharon Robinson

84

87

88

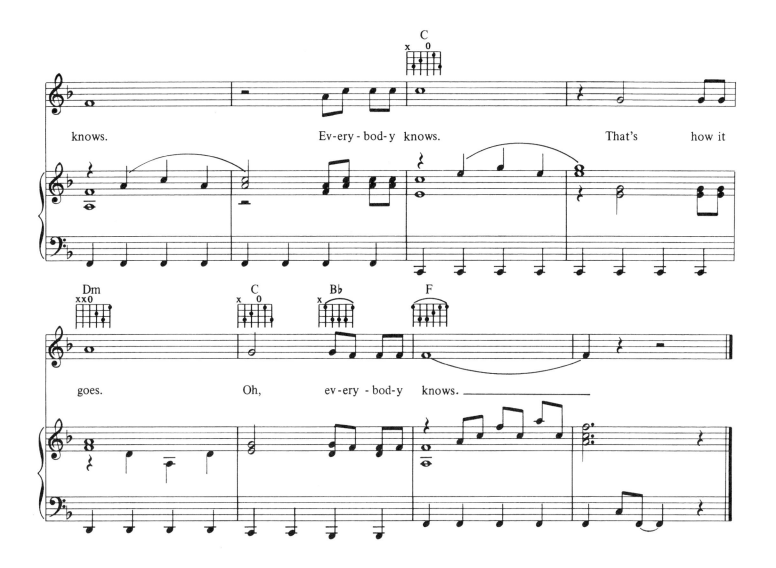

Additional Lyrics

4. And everybody knows that it's now or never.
   Everybody knows that it's me or you.
   And everybody knows that you live forever
   When you've done a line or two.
   Everybody knows the deal is rotten:
   Old Black Joe's still pickin' cotton
   For your ribbons and bows. And everybody knows.

5. Everybody knows that the plague is coming.
   Everybody knows thats it's moving fast.
   Everybody knows that the naked man and woman
   Are just a shining artifact of the past.
   Everybody knows the scene is dead,
   But there's gonna be a meter on your bed
   That will disclose what everybody knows.

6. And everybody knows that you're in trouble.
   Everybody knows what you've been through,
   From the bloody cross on top of Calvary
   To the beach of Malibu.
   Everybody knows it's coming apart:
   Take one last look at this Sacred Heart
   Before it blows. And everybody knows.

Ain't No Cure For Love

Words & Music by Leonard Cohen

real. It don't mat-ter how it all went wrong.____ That

don't change____ the way I feel.____ And I can't be-lieve that time's____

____ gon-na heal this wound____ that I'm speak-ing of. There

ain't no cure,____ there ain't no cure,____ There ain't no cure for love.____

(optional pattern)   *(continued)*

(as written)

I'm ach-ing for you ba-by, I can't pre-tend I'm not. I need to see you nak-ed in your bod-y and your thought. And I've got you like a ha-bit,__ and I'll

I see you in the sub-way,___ and I... I see you on the bus.

(optional pattern)   (continued)

I see you ly-ing down with me,___ and I see you wak-ing up.___ I see your hand, I see your hair, your brace-lets and your brush.___ And I

95

All the rock-et ships are climb-ing through the sky, the hol-ly books are o-pen wide.___ The doc-tors work-ing day and night. But they'll nev-er, ev-er find___ that cure for love,___ that cure for love.___ The

repeat and fade

Take This Waltz

Words & Music by Leonard Cohen & Federico Lorca

lob - by with nine hun - dred win - dows.   There's a
bar where the boys have stopped talk - ing.   They've been

tree where the doves go to die.   There's a
sen - tenced to death go by the blues.   Ah, but

piece that was torn   from the morn - ing,   And it
who is it climbs   to your pic - ture   with a

hangs   in the gal - lery of frost.
gar - land of fresh - ly cut tears?

Drag - ging its tail in the sea.

There's a

And I'll

dance with you in Vi - en - na.

I'll be

wear - ing a riv - er's dis - guise.

The

106

hy - a - cinth wild on my shoul - der, My

mouth on the dew of your thighs. And I'll

bur - y my soul ___ in a scrap - book, With the

pho - to - graphs there, ___ and the moss. And I'll

107

Dance Me To The End Of Love

Words & Music by Leonard Cohen

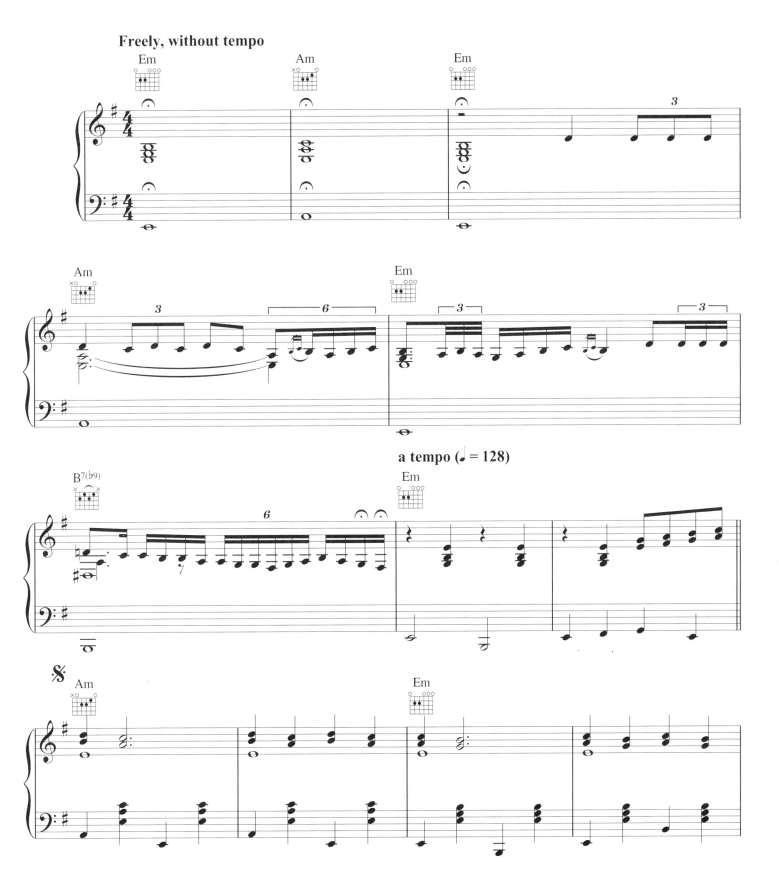

1. Dance me____ to your beau - ty____ with a burn - ing vi - o - lin.
3. Dance me____ to the wed - ding now,____ dance me on and on.
5. Dance me____ to your beau - ty____ with a burn - ing vi - o - lin.

First We Take Manhattan

Words & Music by Leonard Cohen

124

Additional Lyrics

From D.S.
I don't like your fashion business, mister.
I don't like these drugs that keep you thin.
I don't like what happened to my sister.
First we take Manhattan, then we take Berlin.

(Bridge):
I'd really like to live beside you, baby.
I love your body and your spirit and your clothes.
But you see that line there moving through the station?
And I told you, and I told you,
I told you I was one of those,

And I thank you for those items that you sent me:
The monkey and the plywood violin.
I practiced every night and now I'm ready.
First we take Manhattan, then we take Berlin. *(To Coda)*

The Future

Words & Music by Leonard Cohen

Am
- ture.
Give me ab - so - lute con - trol
Dm
G♯°7
o - ver ev - 'ry liv - ing soul, And lie be - side ___ me, ba - by,
E7
Am
that's an or - der!
Dm
Give me crack and a - nal sex, take the on - ly

break - ing of the an - cient West - ern _____ code

Dm

Your pri - vate life will sud - den - ly ex - plode. _

_____ There'll be phan - toms, there'll be fires _

Am

_____ on the road, And the white man

Additional lyrics

2. You don't know me from the wind,
   You never will, you never did,
   I'm the little Jew who wrote the Bible.

   I've seen nations rise and fall,
   I've heard their stories, heard them all,
   But love's the only engine of survival.

   Your servant here, he has been told
   To say it clear, to say it cold:
   It's over, it ain't goin' any further.

   But now the wheels of heaven stop,
   You feel the devil's ridin' crop,
   Get ready for the future: it is murder.
   (Chorus)

3. Give me back the Berlin wall,
   Give me Stalin and St. Paul,
   Give me Christ or give me Hiroshima.

   Destroy another fetus now,
   We don't like children anyhow,
   I've seen the future, baby: it is murder.
   (Chorus, al Coda)

135

Democracy

Words & Music by Leonard Cohen

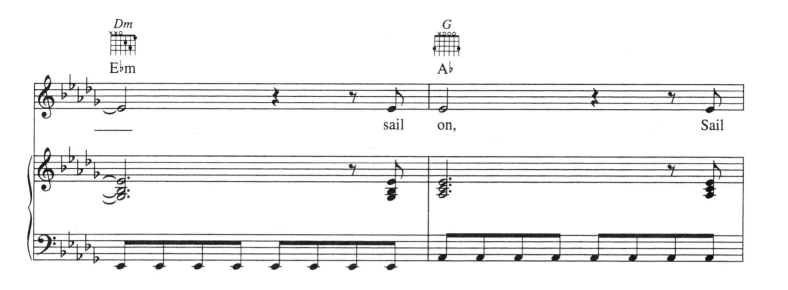

sail on,   Sail

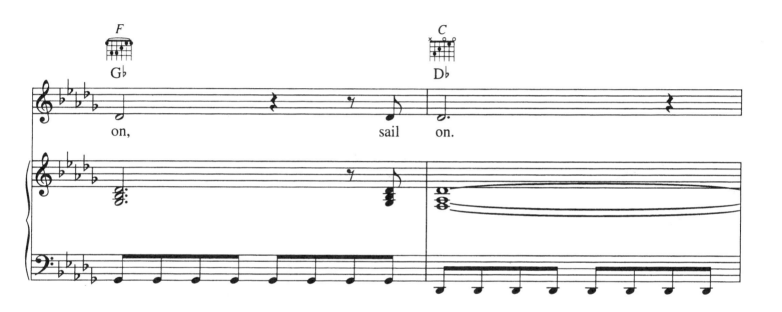

on,   sail on.

1st time: D. S. to verse 4 (1st ending), then to verse 5 (3rd ending to Chorus)

2nd time: D. S. to verse 6 al Coda ⊕ (see additional lyrics) 𝄋

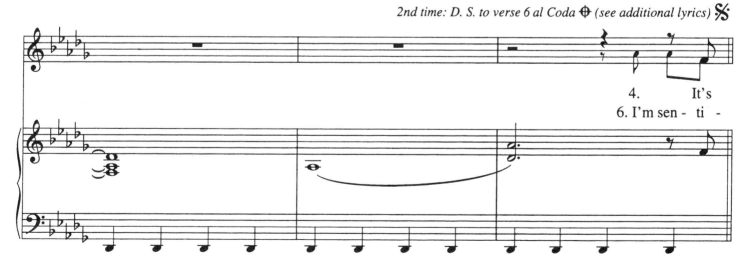

4.   It's

6. I'm sen - ti -

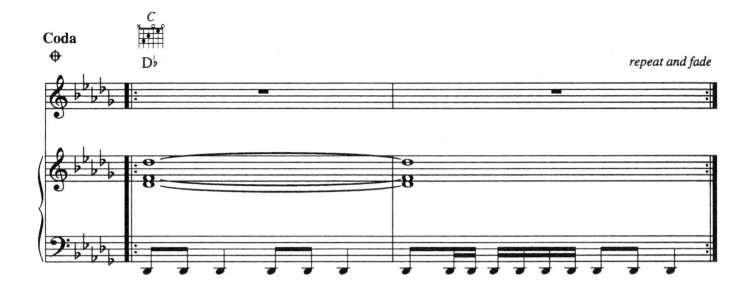

Additional lyrics

2. It's comin' through a crack in the wall
   On a visionary flood of alcohol,
   From the staggering account of the Sermon on the Mount
   Which I don't pretend to understand at all.
   It's comin' from the silence
   On the dock of the bay,
   From the brave, the bold, the battered
   Heart of Chevrolet:
   Democracy is comin' to the U.S.A.

   (to 2nd ending)

3. It's comin' from the sorrow in the street,
   The holy places where the races meet,
   From the homicidal bitchin'
   That goes down in every kitchen
   To determine who will serve and who will eat.
   From the wells of disappointment
   Where the women kneel to pray
   For the Grace of God in the desert here
   And the desert far away:
   Democracy is comin' to the U.S.A.

   (to 3rd ending and Chorus)

(𝄋) 4. It's comin' to America first,
        The cradle of the best and of the worst.
        It's here they got the range
        And the machinery for change,
        And it's here they got the spiritual thirst.
        It's here the family's broken
        And it's here the lonely say
        That the heart has got to open
        In a fundamental way:
        Democracy is comin' to the U.S.A.

(to 1st ending)

5. It's comin' from the women and the men.
        Oh baby, we'll be makin' love again.
        We'll be goin' down so deep,
        The river's goin' to weep,
        And the mountain's goin' to shout, "Amen!"
        It's comin' like the tidal flood
        Beneath the lunar sway,
        Imperial, mysterious,
        In amorous array:
        Democracy is comin' to the U.S.A.

(to 3rd ending and Chorus)

(𝄋) 6. I'm sentimental, if you know what I mean.
        I love the country but I can't stand the scene.
        And I'm neither left or right,
        I'm just stayin' home tonight,
        Gettin' lost in that hopeless little screen.
        But I'm stubborn as those garbage bags
        That Time cannot decay,
        I'm junk but I'm still holdin' up this little wild bouquet:
        Democracy is comin' to the U.S.A.

(Coda ⊕)

Waiting For The Miracle

Words & Music by Leonard Cohen & Sharon Robinson

1. Ba - by, I've been wait - in', I've been wait - in' night and

2., 3., 4., 5., 6. (See additional lyrics)

150

repeat and fade

Additional lyrics

2. I know you really loved me,
   But, you see, my hands were tied.
   And I know it must have hurt you,
   It must have hurt your pride
   To have to stand beneath my window
   With your bugle and your drum,
   And me, I'm up there waitin'
   For the miracle, for the miracle to come.

   (to 2nd ending)

3. I don't believe you'd like it,
   You wouldn't like it here.
   There ain't no entertainment,
   And the judgments are severe.
   The Maestro says it's Mozart,
   But it sounds like bubble gum,
   When you're waitin'
   For the miracle, for the miracle to come.

   (3rd ending to Chorus I)

𝄋 4. Now I dreamed about you, baby,
   It was just the other night.
   Most of you was naked,
   Ah, but some of you was light.
   The sands of time were fallin'
   From your fingers and your thumb,
   And you were waitin'
   For the miracle, for the miracle to come.

   (to 1st ending)

𝄋 5. Now baby, let's get married,
   We've been alone too long
   Let's be alone together,
   Let's see if we're that strong.
   Yeah, let's do somethin' crazy,
   Somethin' absolutely wrong,
   While we're waitin'
   For the miracle, for the miracle to come.

   (to Coda 1 ⊕)

𝄋 6. When you've fallen on the highway,
   And you're lyin' in the rain,
   And they ask you how you're doin',
   Of course, you say you can't complain.
   If you're squeezed for information,
   That's when you've got to play it dumb,
   You just say you're out there waitin'
   For the miracle, for the miracle to come.

   *(to Coda 2 ⊕ ⊕,
   then instrumental fade)*

Closing Time

Words & Music by Leonard Cohen

Moderately slow country beat

(optional 8th note pattern, continued throughout)

clos - in' time.   2. And I
clos - in' time.   3. I
clos - in'   time.

Additional lyrics

2. Ah, we're lonely, we're romantic,
 And the cider laced with acid,
 And the Holy Spirit's cryin', "Where's the beef?"

 And the moon is swimmin' naked,
 And the summer night is fragrant
 With a mighty expectation of relief.

 So we strugle and we stagger
 Down the snakes and up the ladder
 To the tower where the blessed hours chime.

 And I swear it happened just like this:
 A sigh, a cry, a hungry kiss,
 The gates of love, they budged an inch,
 I can't say much has happened since
 But closing time.

 I swear it happened just like this:
 A sigh, a cry. a hungry kiss,
 The gates of love, they budged an inch,
 I can't say much has happened since...   *(to 2nd ending)*

3. Yeah, we're drinkin' and we're dancin',
 But there's nothin' really happenin',
 And the place is dead as Heaven on a Saturday night.

 And my very close companion
 Gets me fumblin', gets me laughin',
 She's a hundred but she's wearin' somethin' tight.

 And I lift my glass to the Awful Truth
 Which you can't reveal to the ears of youth,
 Except to say it isn't worth a dime.

 And the whole damn place goes crazy twice,
 And it's once for the Devil and it's once for Christ,
 But the Boss don't like these dizzy heights,
 We're busted in the blindin' lights
 Of closin' time.

 The whole damn place goes crazy twice,
 And it's once for the devil and it's once for Christ,
 But the Boss don't like these dizzy heights,
 We're busted in the blindin' lights...   *(to Coda ⊕)*

164

Alexandra Leaving

Words & Music by Sharon Robinson & Leonard Cohen

169

Anthem

Words & Music by Leonard Cohen

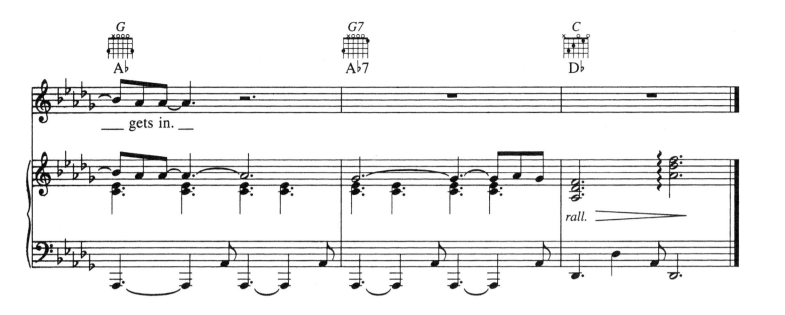

gets in.

Additional lyrics

2. We asked for signs, the signs were sent,
    The birth betrayed, the marriage spent.
    Yeah, the widowhood of every government,
    Signs for all to see.

    I can't run no more with that lawless crowd
    While the killers in high places say their prayers out loud.
    But they've summoned, they've summoned up a thundercloud,
    They're going to hear from me.

    (Chorus to 2nd ending)

In My Secret Life

Words & Music by Leonard Cohen & Sharon Robinson

Love Itself

Words & Music by Sharon Robinson & Leonard Cohen

1. The light came through the win-dow

straight from the___ sun a - bove,

and so in - side_____ my lit - tle room___

there plunged the rays of_____ love.

2. In streams of light_____ I clear - ly saw___
3,. 4. All bu - sy in the sun - light,___

love went on and on

un - til it reached an op - en door; then

love it - self, love it - self was

gone.

1.

To Coda ⊕

187

A Thousand Kisses Deep

Words & Music by Sharon Robinson & Leonard Cohen

And some-times when the night is slow,

the wretch-ed and the meek,___ we gath-er up our hearts and___

go a thou-sand kiss-es deep.

3. Con - fined to
5. The pon - ies

(3.) sex we pressed a - gainst the li - mits of the sea.
(4.) tricks, I'm get - ting fixed, I'm back on Boo - gie Street.
(5.) run, the girls are young, the odds are there to beat.

I saw there were no o - ceans left
I guess they won't ex - change the gifts that you were
You win a while and then it's done, your lit - tle

for sca - veng - ers like me. I made it to the for - ward
meant to keep. And qui - et is the thought of
win - ning streak. And sum - moned now to deal

deck,
you,
____ with your

I blessed our rem - nant fleet,____
the file on you com - plete,____
in - vin - ci - ble de - feat,____

and then con -
ex - cept what
you live your

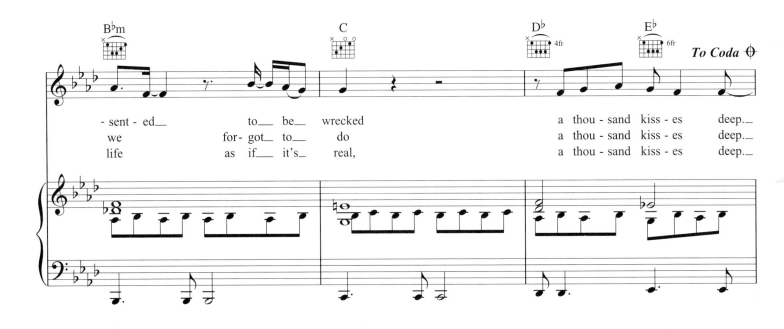

- sent - ed____
we for - got__ to__
life as if__ it's__

to__ be__ wrecked
do
real,

a thou - sand kiss - es deep.__
a thou - sand kiss - es deep.__
a thou - sand kiss - es deep.__

To Coda ✛

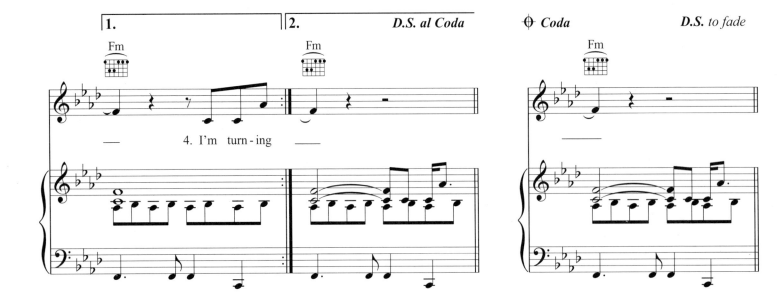

1.   2.   *D.S. al Coda*   ✛ *Coda*   *D.S. to fade*

____ 4. I'm turn - ing ____

Printed in Malta by Progress Press Co. Ltd   9/08 (166845)